THE GOLD BOOK

six chord song book

Wise Publications
London/New York/Sydney/ Paris/Copenhagen/Madrid/Tokyo

The *Six Chord Songbook Gold* allows even the beginner guitarist to play and enjoy the best rock and pop tunes. With the maximum of 6 chords for each song, you'll soon master playing your favourite hits.

The *Six Chord Songbook* doesn't use musical notation. Throughout the book chord boxes are printed at the head of each song; the chord changes are shown above the lyrics. It's left up to you, the guitarist, to decide on a strum rhythm or picking pattern.

You might find the pitch of the vocal line is not always comfortable because it is pitched too high or two low. In that case, you can change the key without learning a new set of chords; simply place a capo behind a suitable fret.

Whatever you do, this *Six Chord Songbook* guarantees hours of enjoyment for guitarists of all levels, as well as providing a fine basis for building a strong repertoire.

Exclusive distributors:
Music Sales Limited
8/9 Frith Street,
London W1D 3JB, England.
Music Sales Pty Limited
120 Rothschild Avenue
Rosebery, NSW 2018,
Australia.

Order No.AM958991
ISBN 0-7119-8201-5
This book © Copyright 2000 by Wise Publications

Compiled by Nick Crispin
Music processed by The Pitts
Cover design by Chloë Alexander
Photographs courtesy of London Features International

Printed in the United Kingdom by
Printwise (Haverhill) Limited, Suffolk.

Music Sales' complete catalogue describes thousands of titles
and is available in full colour sections by subject, direct from
Music Sales Limited. Please state your areas of interest and
send a cheque/postal order for £1.50 for postage to:
Music Sales Limited, Newmarket Road, Bury St. Edmunds, Suffolk IP33 3YB.

www.musicsales.com

Relative Tuning

The guitar can be tuned with the aid of pitch pipes or dedicated electronic guitar tuners which are available through your local music dealer. If you do not have a tuning device, you can use relative tuning. Estimate the pitch of the 6th string as near as possible to E or at least a comfortable pitch (not too high, as you might break other strings in tuning up). Then, while checking the various positions on the diagram, place a finger from your left hand on the:

5th fret of the E or 6th string and **tune the open A** (or 5th string) to the note (A)

5th fret of the A or 5th string and **tune the open D** (or 4th string) to the note (D)

5th fret of the D or 4th string and **tune the open G** (or 3rd string) to the note (G)

4th fret of the G or 3rd string and **tune the open B** (or 2nd string) to the note (B)

5th fret of the B or 2nd string and **tune the open E** (or 1st string) to the note (E)

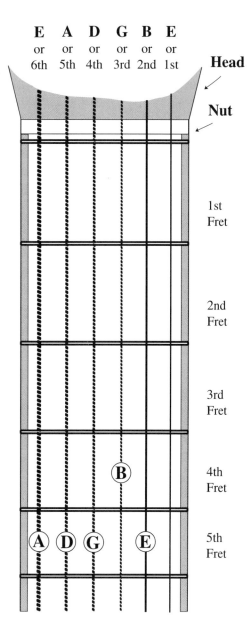

Reading Chord Boxes

Chord boxes are diagrams of the guitar neck viewed head upwards, face on as illustrated. The top horizontal line is the nut, unless a higher fret number is indicated, the others are the frets.

The vertical lines are the strings, starting from E (or 6th) on the left to E (or 1st) on the right.

The black dots indicate where to place your fingers.

Strings marked with an O are played open, not fretted.

Strings marked with an X should not be played.

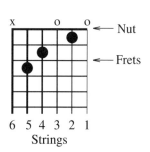

Cast No Shadow

Words & Music by
Noel Gallagher

Asus⁴   G   Em   D   C   Cmaj⁷

Intro ‖: **Asus⁴** | **Asus⁴** | **G** | **G** :‖

Verse 1

Asus⁴
Here's a thought for every man

                                                     G
Who tries to understand what is in his hands.

Asus⁴
He walks along the open road of love and life

                   G
Surviving if he can.

Em   **D**
Bound with all the weight

               C   **G**
Of all the words he tried to say.

Em   **D**
Chained to all the places

            C   **G**
That he never wished to stay.

Em   **D**
Bound with all the weight

             C   **G**
Of all the words he tried to say.

Em   **D**   **C**
As he faced the sun he cast no shadow.

Chorus 1

G   **Asus⁴**   **Cmaj⁷** | **Em** **D** |
As they took his soul they stole his pride,

G   **Asus⁴**   **Cmaj⁷** | **Em** **D** |
As they took his soul they stole his pride,

G   **Asus⁴**   **Cmaj⁷** | **Em** **D** |
As they took his soul they stole his pride,

Em   **D**   **C** | **C** | **C** | **Asus⁴** ‖
As he faced the sun he cast no shadow.

Verse 2   As Verse 1

Chorus 2
G   Asus4   Cmaj7 | Em D |
As they took his soul they stole his pride,
G   Asus4   Cmaj7 | Em D |
As they took his soul they stole his pride,
G   Asus4   Cmaj7 | Em D |
As they took his soul they stole his pride,
G   Asus4   Cmaj7 | Em D |
As they took his soul they took his pride.

Outro
Em   D   C | C |
As he faced the sun he cast no shadow,
Em   D   C | C |
As he faced the sun he cast no shadow,
Em   D   C | C |
As he faced the sun he cast no shadow,
Em   D   C | C |
As he faced the sun he cast no shadow.

| C | C | C | G ‖

Cloud Number Nine

Words & Music by
Bryan Adams, Max Martin & Gretchen Peters

| D | G | Bm7 | Asus4 | Em | A |

Intro
| (D) | (D) ‖ D | D | G | G |
| Bm7 | Bm7 | Asus4 | Asus4 | G | G | D | D ‖

Verse 1

(D)
Clue number one was when you knocked on my door,
(G)
Clue number two was the look that you wore,
(Em)
And that's when I knew it was a pretty good sign
(G) **(D)**
That something was wrong up on cloud number nine.

Pre-chorus 1

Bm7
Well it's a long way up

D
And we won't come down tonight,
Bm7
Well it may be wrong

G   A
But baby it sure feels right.

Chorus 1

D
And the moon is out and the stars are bright
Em
And whatever comes gonna be alright,
A   **G**   **D**
'Cause tonight you will be mine   up on cloud number nine.
Bm7
And there ain't no place that I'd rather be,
Em
And we can't go back but you're here with me.
A   **G**   **D**
Yeah, the weather is really fine   up on cloud number nine.

Verse 2

      D
Now he hurt you and you hurt me

      Em
And that wasn't the way it was supposed to be,

      Asus4   **A**
So baby tonight let's leave the   world behind

     G   **D**
And spend some time up on cloud number nine.

Pre-chorus 2   As Pre-chorus 1

Chorus 2   As Chorus 1

Link | **D** | **D** | **G** | **G** | **Bm7** | **Bm7** |

          | **Asus4** | **Asus4** | **G** | **G** ||

              A
Bridge   Well we won't come down tonight,

Yeah, we won't come down tonight,

No, we won't come down tonight.

               D
Chorus 3   'Cause the moon is out and the stars are bright

        Em
And whatever comes gonna be alright,

          A   **G**   **D**
'Cause tonight you will be mine   up on cloud number nine.

          Bm7
And there ain't no place that I'd rather be,

          Em
And we can't go back but you're here with me.

          A   **G**   **D**
Yeah, the weather is really fine up on cloud number nine.

N.C.
Yeah, we can watch the world go by up on cloud number nine.

Driftwood

Words & Music by
Fran Healy

Em   A   D   G6   Asus4   A7

Capo seventh fret

Intro | (Em) | (A) | Em | A ||

Verse 1
D   G6   Asus4   A
Everything is open, nothing is set in stone.
D   G6   Asus4   A
Rivers turn to oceans, oceans tide you home.
D   G6   Asus4   A
Home is where the heart is, but your heart had to roam,
D   G6   Asus4   A
Drifting over bridges never to return,
A7
Watching bridges burn.

Chorus 1
               D   A   Em
You're driftwood floating underwater,
                  G6
Breaking into pieces, pieces, pieces.
         D   A   Em
Just driftwood, hollow and of no use,
                G6
Waterfalls will find you, bind you, grind you.

Verse 2
D   G6   Asus4   A
Nobody is an island, everyone has to go.
D   G6   Asus4   A
Pillars turn to butter, butterflying low.
D   G6   Asus4   A
Low is where your heart is but your heart has to grow,
D   G6   Asus4   A
Drifting under bridges, never with the flow.

Pre-chorus 1

             Em   Asus4   A
And you really didn't think it would happen
             Em   Asus4   A
But it really is the end of the line.

Chorus 2

                  D   A   Em
So I'm sorry that you've turned to driftwood
                    G6   D
But you've been drifting for a long, long time.

Solo

| Em | Asus4 A | Em | Asus4 A |

| Em | Asus4 A | Em | Em |

Verse 3

D   G6   Asus4   A
Everywhere there's trouble, nowhere's safe to go.
D   G6   Asus4   A
Pushes turn to shovels, shovelling the snow.
D   G6   Asus4   A
Frozen you have chosen the path you wish to go,
D   G6 Asus4   A
Drifting now forever and forever more
      A7
Until you reach your shore.

Chorus 3

                D   A   Em
You're driftwood floating underwater,
                    G6
Breaking into pieces, pieces, pieces.
            D   A   Em
Just driftwood, hollow and of no use,
                    G6
Waterfalls will find you, bind you, grind you.

Pre-chorus 2

             Em   Asus4   A
And you really didn't think it would happen
            Em   Asus4   A
But it really is the end of the line.

Chorus 4

                  D   A   Em
So I'm sorry that you've turned to driftwood
                    G6   D
But you've been drifting for a long, long time,
                    Em   D
But you've been drifting for a long, long time,
                Em   G6   D
You've been drifting for a long, long, drifting for a long, long time.

Everybody's Talkin'

Words & Music by
Fred Neil

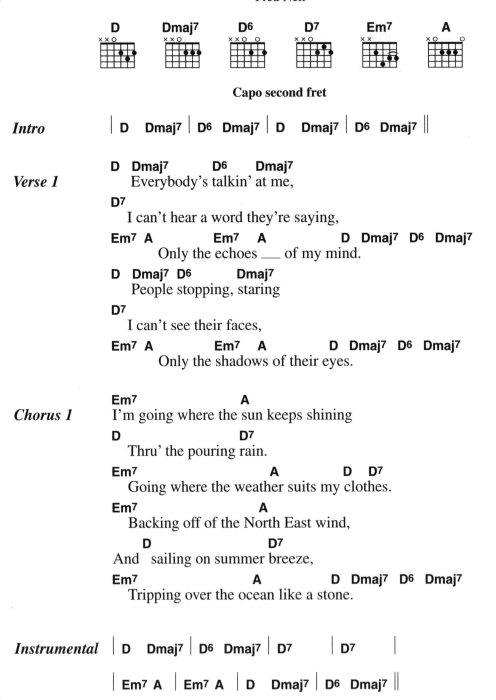

Capo second fret

Intro ‖ D   Dmaj7 │ D6   Dmaj7 │ D   Dmaj7 │ D6   Dmaj7 ‖

Verse 1

D   Dmaj7   D6   Dmaj7
Everybody's talkin' at me,

D7
I can't hear a word they're saying,

Em7 A   Em7   A   D Dmaj7 D6 Dmaj7
Only the echoes ___ of my mind.

D Dmaj7 D6   Dmaj7
People stopping, staring

D7
I can't see their faces,

Em7 A   Em7   A   D Dmaj7 D6 Dmaj7
Only the shadows of their eyes.

Chorus 1

Em7   A
I'm going where the sun keeps shining

D   D7
Thru' the pouring rain.

Em7   A   D   D7
Going where the weather suits my clothes.

Em7   A
Backing off of the North East wind,

D   D7
And   sailing on summer breeze,

Em7   A   D Dmaj7 D6 Dmaj7
Tripping over the ocean like a stone.

Instrumental │ D   Dmaj7 │ D6 Dmaj7 │ D7   │ D7   │

│ Em7 A │ Em7 A │ D   Dmaj7 │ D6   Dmaj7 ‖

Chorus 2

Em⁷   A
I'm going where the sun keeps shining

D   D⁷
  Thru' the pouring rain.

Em⁷   A   D   D⁷
  Going where the weather suits my clothes.

Em⁷   A
  Backing off of the North East wind,

        D   D⁷
And   sailing on summer breeze,

Em⁷   A   D   Dmaj⁷   D⁶   Dmaj⁷
  Tripping over the ocean like a stone.

D   Dmaj⁷   D⁶   Dmaj⁷   D   Dmaj⁷   D⁶   Dmaj⁷
  Everybody's talkin' at me. _____

‖: D   Dmaj⁷ | D⁶ Dmaj⁷ | D   Dmaj⁷ | D⁶ Dmaj⁷ |

| D   Dmaj⁷ | D⁶ Dmaj⁷ | D   Dmaj⁷ | D⁶ Dmaj⁷ :‖ D   ‖

Father And Son

Words & Music by
Cat Stevens

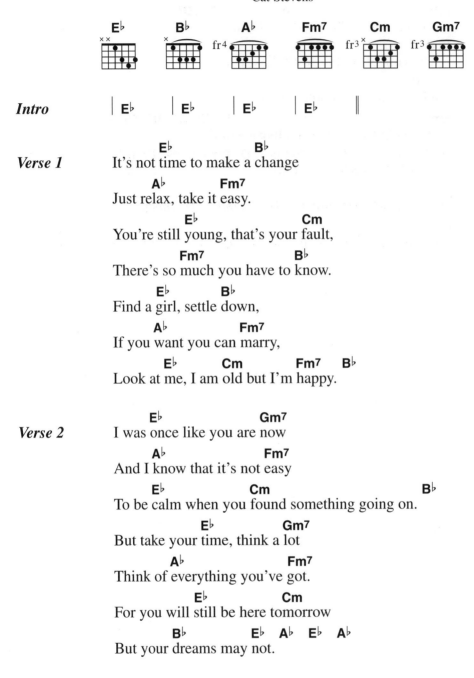

Intro

| E♭ | E♭ | E♭ | E♭ ‖

Verse 1

      E♭   B♭
It's not time to make a change

   A♭   Fm7
Just relax, take it easy.

       E♭   Cm
You're still young, that's your fault,

     Fm7   B♭
There's so much you have to know.

    E♭   B♭
Find a girl, settle down,

     A♭   Fm7
If you want you can marry,

     E♭   Cm   Fm7 B♭
Look at me, I am old but I'm happy.

Verse 2

     E♭   Gm7
I was once like you are now

   A♭   Fm7
And I know that it's not easy

    E♭   Cm   B♭
To be calm when you found something going on.

      E♭   Gm7
But take your time, think a lot

    A♭   Fm7
Think of everything you've got.

    E♭   Cm
For you will still be here tomorrow

   B♭   E♭ A♭ E♭ A♭
But your dreams may not.

Verse 3

       E♭   Gm7
How can I try to explain?
       A♭   Fm7
When I do he turns away again;
       E♭   Cm   Fm7 B♭
Well, it's always been the same, same old story.
       E♭   Gm7
From the moment I could talk
       A♭   Fm7
I was ordered to listen,
       E♭   Cm
Now there's a way and I know
       B♭   E♭
That I have to go away.
       B♭   A♭   E♭ A♭ E♭ A♭
I know I have to go.

Verse 4

       E♭   B♭
It's not time to make a change
       A♭   Fm7
Just sit down and take it slowly
       E♭   Cm
You're still young, that's your fault
       Fm7   B♭
There's so much you have to go through.
       E♭   Gm7
Find a girl, settle down
       A♭   Fm7
If you want you can marry
       E♭   Cm   Fm7 B♭
Look at me, I am old but I'm happy.

Verse 5

       E♭   Gm7
All the times that I've cried
       A♭   Fm7
Keeping all the things I know inside;
       E♭   Cm7   Fm7 B♭
And it's hard, but it's harder to ignore it.
       E♭   Gm7
If they were right I'd agree
       A♭   Fm7
But it's them they know not me;
       E♭   Cm
Now there's a way, and I know
       B♭   E♭
That I have to go away.
       B♭   A♭   E♭
I know I have to go.

Fields Of Gold

Words & Music by
Sting

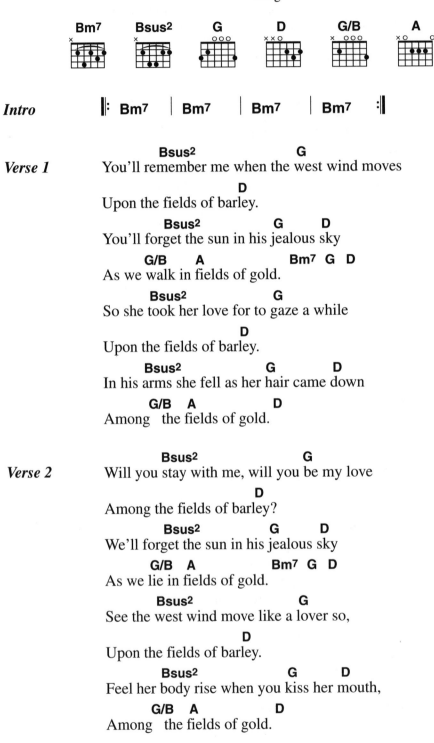

Intro   ‖: Bm7 | Bm7 | Bm7 | Bm7 :‖

Verse 1

       Bsus2   **G**
You'll remember me when the west wind moves
               D
Upon the fields of barley.
       Bsus2   **G**   **D**
You'll forget the sun in his jealous sky
   G/B   **A**   **Bm7 G D**
As we walk in fields of gold.
       Bsus2   **G**
So she took her love for to gaze a while
               D
Upon the fields of barley.
       Bsus2   **G**   **D**
In his arms she fell as her hair came down
   G/B **A**   **D**
Among   the fields of gold.

Verse 2

       Bsus2   **G**
Will you stay with me, will you be my love
               D
Among the fields of barley?
       Bsus2   **G**   **D**
We'll forget the sun in his jealous sky
   G/B **A**   **Bm7 G D**
As we lie in fields of gold.
       Bsus2   **G**
See the west wind move like a lover so,
               D
Upon the fields of barley.
       Bsus2   **G**   **D**
Feel her body rise when you kiss her mouth,
   G/B **A**   **D**
Among   the fields of gold.

Middle

```
G               D
I never made promises lightly,
G                       D
And there have been some that I've broken,
G                   D
But I swear in the days still left
            G/B  A           D
We'll walk   in fields of gold,
        G/B     A           D
We'll walk in fields of gold.
```

Instrumental ‖ **Bsus²** | **G** | **G** | **D** |

| **Bsus²** | **G**   **D** | **G/B** **A** | **D**   ‖

Verse 3

```
        Bsus²                      G
Many years have passed since those summer days
                    D
Among the fields of barley.
          Bsus²               G       D
See the children run as the sun goes down
      G/B     A           D
Among   the fields of gold.
          Bsus²               G
You'll remember me when the west wind moves
                    D
Upon the fields of barley.
          Bsus²               G       D
You can tell the sun in his jealous sky
          G/B         A           D
When we walked in fields of gold,
          G/B         A           D
When we walked in fields of gold,
          G/B         A
When we walked in fields of gold.
```

Instrumental ‖ **D**   **G**   **D**| **D**   **G**   **D** | **D**   **G**   **D**| **D**   **G**   **D**|

| **D**   **G**   **D**| **D**   **G**   **D** | **D**   **G**   **D**| **D**   ‖

Get Back

Words & Music by
John Lennon & Paul McCartney

A5   G   D/A   D   A7   D7

Intro | A5 | A5 | A5 | A5 G D/A ||

Verse 1

A5
Jojo was a man who thought he was a loner
D   A5
But he knew it couldn't last.

Jojo left his home in Tucson, Arizona
D   A5
For some California grass.

Chorus 1

A7
Get back, get back,
D7   A5   G D/A
Get back to where you once belonged.
A7
Get back, get back,
D7   A5
Get back to where you once belonged.

Get back Jojo.

Solo ||: (A5) | A5 | D | A5 G D/A :||

Chorus 2

A7
Get back, get back,
D7   A5   G D/A
Get back to where you once belonged.
A7
Get back, get back,
A5   D
Get back to where you once belonged.
A5
Get back Jo.

Solo ‖: (A5) | A5 | D | A5 G D/A :‖

Verse 2

A5
Sweet Loretta Martin thought she was a woman
D   A5
But she was another man.

All the girls around her say she's got it coming
D   A5
But she gets it while she can.

Chorus 3

A7
Get back, get back,
D7   A5   G D/A
Get back to where you once belonged.
A7
Get back, get back,
D7   A5
Get back to where you once belonged.

Get back Loretta.

Solo ‖: A5 | A5 | D | A5 G D/A :‖

Chorus 4

A7
Get back, get back,
D7   A5   G D/A
Get back to where you once belonged.
A7
Get back, get back,
D7   D
Get back to where you once belonged.   Ooh.

‖: A5 | A5 | D | A5 G D/A :‖ *Repeat to fade*
Get back.

Livin' On A Prayer

Words & Music by
Jon Bon Jovi, Richie Sambora & Desmond Child

Em   C/E   D/E   C   D   G

Verse 1

Em
Tommy used to work on the docks,

                                                 C/E   D/E
Union's been on strike, he's down on his luck, it's tough,

Em
So tough.

Gina works the diner all day,

                                           C/E   D/E
Working for her man, she brings home her pay for love,

Em
For love.

Bridge 1

                        C   D   Em
She says we've got to hold on to what we've got,

  C   D   Em
It doesn't make a difference if we make it or not,

          C   D   Em   C
We've got each other and that's a lot for love,

    D
We'll give it a shot.

Chorus 1

Em C   D
Oh,   we're half way there,

G C D
Oh,   livin' on a prayer,

Em   C   D
Take my hand, we'll make it I swear,

G C D   Em
Oh,   livin' on a prayer.

Verse 2

Em
Tommy got his six-string in hock,

                       C/E   D/E
Now he's holding in when he used to make it talk so tough,

   Em
It's tough.

Gina dreams of running away,

                        C/E   D/E
When she cries in the night Tommy whispers "Baby, it's o.k."

   Em
Some day.

Bridge 2

As Bridge 1

Chorus 2

Em C   D
Oh, we're half way there,

G C D
Oh, livin' on a prayer,

Em   C   D
Take my hand, we'll make it I swear,

G C D
Oh, livin' on a prayer,

C
Livin' on a prayer.

Guitar solo

| Em C | D | | G C | D | |

| Em C | D | | G C | Em | |

Em   C D   Em
We've got to hold on, ready or not,

    C   D
You live for the fight when that's all you've got.

Ad lib. to fade

Linger

Words by Dolores O'Riordan
Music by Dolores O'Riordan & Noel Hogan

Dadd11 D A6 C Cmaj7 G

Intro

‖: Dadd11 | D | Dadd4 | D :‖ Dadd11 ‖

| A6 | A6 | C Cmaj7 | C Cmaj7 | G | G ‖

Verse 1

    D
If you, if you could return,

       A6
Don't let it burn, don't let it fade.

         C
I'm sure I'm not being rude,

But it's just your attitude,

       G
It's tearing me apart,

It's ruining ev'rything.

Verse 2

    D
I swore, I swore I would be true,

      A6
And honey, so did you,

        C
So why were you holding her hand?

Is that the way we stand?

      G
Were you lying all the time?

Was it just a game to you?

Chorus 1

               D
But I'm in so deep,

                       A6
You know I'm such a fool for you,

                                     C   **Cmaj7**
You got me wrapped around your finger, ah, ah, ha.

C   **G**
  Do you have to let it linger?

Do you have to, do you have to,

                    D
Do you have to let it linger?

Middle

             A6
Oh, I thought the world of you,

                  C   **Cmaj7**   **C**
I thought nothing could go wrong,

Cmaj7   **G**
But I was wrong, I was wrong.

Verse 3

            D
If you, if you could get by

                A6
Trying not to lie,

                               C
Things wouldn't get so confused,

And I wouldn't feel so used,

                       G
But you always really knew

I just wanna be with you.

Chorus 2

               D
But I'm in so deep,

                       A6
You know I'm such a fool for you,

                                       C   **Cmaj7**
You got me wrapped around your finger, ah, ah, ha.

C   **G**
  Do you have to let it linger?

Do you have to, do you have to,

                    D
Do you have to let it linger?

Solo | D | D | A6 | A6 | C Cmaj7 | C Cmaj7 | G | G   ‖

Chorus 3　　　　　　D
But I'm in so deep,

　　　　　　　　　　A6
You know I'm such a fool for you,

　　　　　　　　　　　　　　C　　　Cmaj7
You got me wrapped around your finger, ah, ah, ha.

C　　　　　　　　　　　G
　Do you have to let it linger?

Do you have to, do you have to,

　　　　　　　　　　D
Do you have to let it linger?

　　　　　　　　　　A6
Chorus 4　　You know I'm such a fool for you,

　　　　　　　　　　　　　C　　　Cmaj7
You got me wrapped around your finger, ah, ah, ha.

C　　　　　　　　　　G
　Do you have to let it linger?

Do you have to, do you have to,

　　　　　　　　　　D
Do you have to let it linger?

Instrumental | D　　| D　　| A6　| A6　| C　Cmaj7 | C　Cmaj7 | G　　| G　　|

| D　　| D　Dadd11 | D　　| D　Dadd11 | D　　| D　Dadd11 | D　‖

22

Romeo And Juliet

Words & Music by
Mark Knopfler

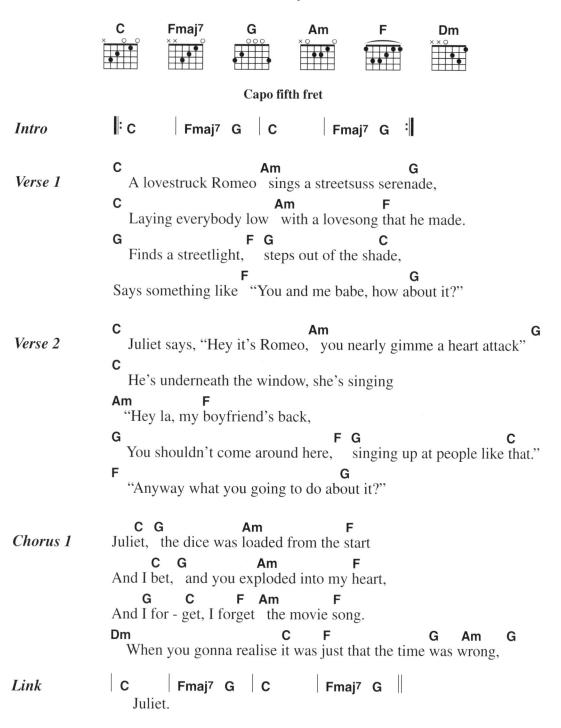

C   Fmaj7   G   Am   F   Dm

Capo fifth fret

Intro

‖: C | Fmaj7 G | C | Fmaj7 G :‖

Verse 1

C   Am   G
A lovestruck Romeo sings a streetsuss serenade,
C   Am   F
Laying everybody low with a lovesong that he made.
G   F G   C
Finds a streetlight,   steps out of the shade,
                    F   G
Says something like "You and me babe, how about it?"

Verse 2

C   Am   G
Juliet says, "Hey it's Romeo, you nearly gimme a heart attack"
C
He's underneath the window, she's singing
Am   F
"Hey la, my boyfriend's back,
G   F G   C
You shouldn't come around here,   singing up at people like that."
F   G
"Anyway what you going to do about it?"

Chorus 1

      C G   Am   F
Juliet, the dice was loaded from the start
         C   G   Am   F
And I bet, and you exploded into my heart,
      G   C   F Am   F
And I for - get, I forget the movie song.
Dm   C   F   G   Am   G
When you gonna realise it was just that the time was wrong,

Link

| C | Fmaj7 G | C | Fmaj7 G ‖
Juliet.

Verse 3

```
C                        Am                              G
   Come up on different streets,   they both were streets of shame,
C                        Am                    F
   Both dirty, both mean,   yes and the dream was just the same.
G                              F    G              C
   And I dreamed your dream for you   and now your dream is real.
F                                      G
   How can you look at me as if I was just another one of your deals?
```

Verse 4

```
                C                      G
When you can fall for chains of silver,
Am                          G
   You can fall for chains of gold,
C                              Am            F              G
   You can fall for pretty strangers    and the promises they hold.
                          F  G            C
You promised me everything,      you promised me thick and thin,
F
   Now you just say, "Oh Romeo, yeah, you know,
 G
I used to have a scene with him."
```

Chorus 2

```
        C  G           Am              F
Juliet,   when we made love you used to cry.
             C              G            Am          F
You said "I love you like the stars above, I'll love you till I die."
G        C       F   Am                    F
There's a place for us,    you know the movie song,
Dm                        C    F              G    Am   G
   When you gonna realise it was just that the time was wrong,

Juli-(et.)
```

Link

```
| C      | Fmaj7  G  | C      | Fmaj7  G  ||
-et
```

Verse 5

```
C                     Am                         G
   I can't do the talk     like they talk on TV,
C                          Am                F
   And I can't do a love song    like the way it's meant to be,
G                         F   G            C
   I can't do everything but I'd do anything for you,
F                              G
   I can't do anything except be in love with you.
```

Verse 6

  C   Am   G
And all I do is miss you   and the way we used to be,

  C   Am   F
All I do is keep the beat   and bad company,

  G   F
All I do is kiss you

  G   C
Through the bars of a rhyme.

  F   G
Julie, I'd do the stars with you any time.

Chorus 3

      C G   Am   F
Juliet, when we made love you used to cry.

          C   G   Am   F
You said "I love you like the stars above, I'll love you till I die."

  G   C   G F Am   F
There's a place for us,   you know the movie song,

  Dm   C   F   G Am   G
When you gonna realise it was just that the time was wrong,

Ju(-u-u-liet.)

Link

| C | Fmaj7 G | C | Fmaj7 G |
-u-u-liet.

| C | Fmaj7 G | C | Fmaj7 G ‖

Verse 7

  C   Am   G
And a lovestruck Romeo   sings a streetsuss serenade,

  C   Am   F
Laying everybody low   with a lovesong that he made.

  G   F
Finds a convenient streetlight,

  G   C
Steps out of the shade,

                      F   G
Says something like "You and me babe,   how about it?"

Coda   ‖: Fmaj7 | G | Fmaj7 | G :‖ *Repeat ad lib. to fade*

One Way

Words & Music by
Jonathan Sevink, Charles Heather, Simon Friend, Jeremy Cunningham & Mark Chadwick

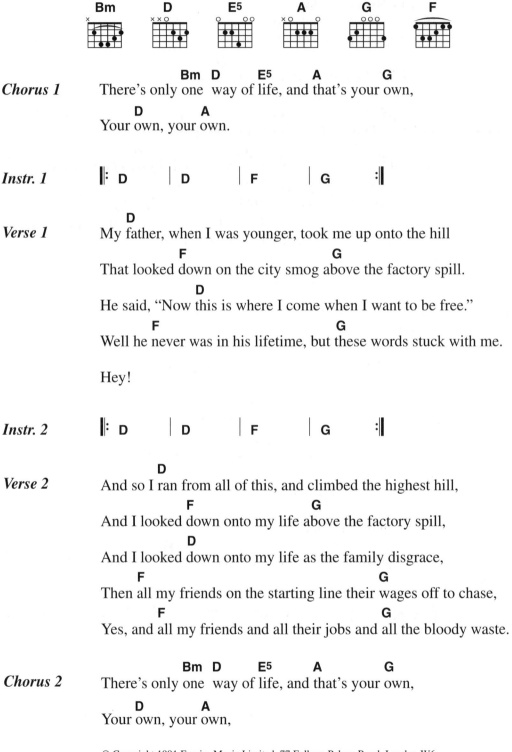

Chorus 1
Bm D   E5   A   G
There's only one way of life, and that's your own,
D   A
Your own, your own.

Instr. 1
‖: D | D | F | G :‖

Verse 1
D
My father, when I was younger, took me up onto the hill
F   G
That looked down on the city smog above the factory spill.
D
He said, "Now this is where I come when I want to be free."
F   G
Well he never was in his lifetime, but these words stuck with me.

Hey!

Instr. 2
‖: D | D | F | G :‖

Verse 2
D
And so I ran from all of this, and climbed the highest hill,
F   G
And I looked down onto my life above the factory spill,
D
And I looked down onto my life as the family disgrace,
F   G
Then all my friends on the starting line their wages off to chase,
F   G
Yes, and all my friends and all their jobs and all the bloody waste.

Chorus 2
Bm D   E5   A   G
There's only one way of life, and that's your own,
D   A
Your own, your own,

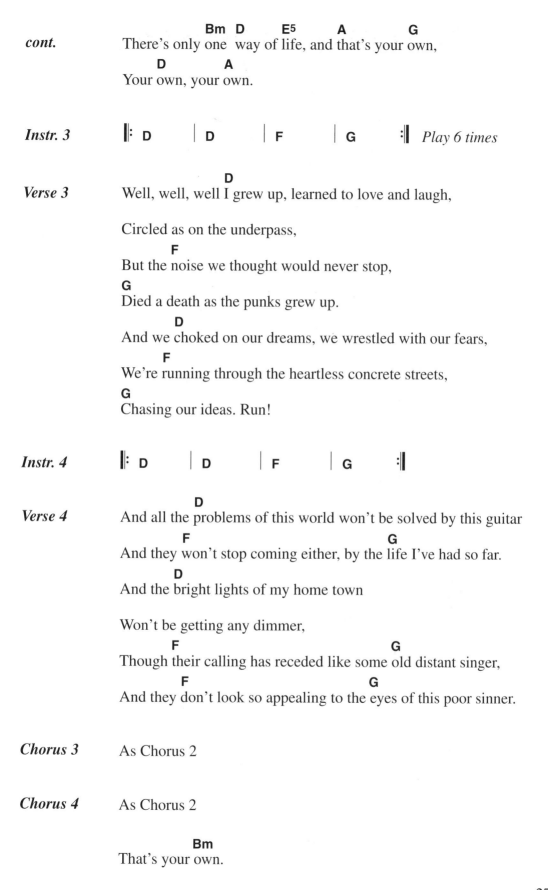

cont.

          Bm D   **E5**   **A**   **G**
There's only one way of life, and that's your own,

      D   **A**
Your own, your own.

Instr. 3   ‖: **D** | **D** | **F** | **G**   :‖ *Play 6 times*

Verse 3

                  D
Well, well, well I grew up, learned to love and laugh,

Circled as on the underpass,

      F
But the noise we thought would never stop,

G
Died a death as the punks grew up.

        D
And we choked on our dreams, we wrestled with our fears,

      F
We're running through the heartless concrete streets,

G
Chasing our ideas. Run!

Instr. 4   ‖: **D** | **D** | **F** | **G**   :‖

Verse 4

            D
And all the problems of this world won't be solved by this guitar

        F   **G**
And they won't stop coming either, by the life I've had so far.

        D
And the bright lights of my home town

Won't be getting any dimmer,

        F   **G**
Though their calling has receded like some old distant singer,

        F   **G**
And they don't look so appealing to the eyes of this poor sinner.

Chorus 3   As Chorus 2

Chorus 4   As Chorus 2

         Bm
That's your own.

Something Changed

Words by Jarvis Cocker
Music by Pulp

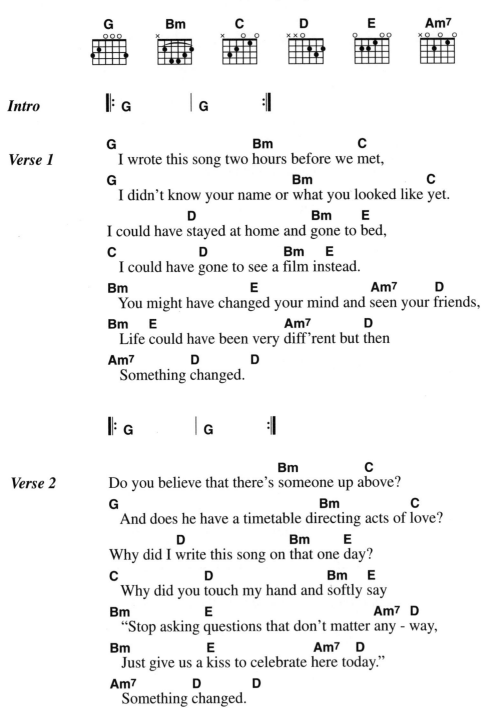

Intro ‖: G | G :‖

Verse 1

G   Bm   C
I wrote this song two hours before we met,

G   Bm   C
I didn't know your name or what you looked like yet.

                D   Bm   E
I could have stayed at home and gone to bed,

C   D   Bm   E
I could have gone to see a film instead.

Bm   E   Am⁷   D
You might have changed your mind and seen your friends,

Bm   E   Am⁷   D
Life could have been very diff'rent but then

Am⁷   D   D
Something changed.

‖: G | G :‖

Verse 2

                             Bm   C
Do you believe that there's someone up above?

G   Bm   C
And does he have a timetable directing acts of love?

                D   Bm   E
Why did I write this song on that one day?

C   D   Bm   E
Why did you touch my hand and softly say

Bm   E   Am⁷ D
"Stop asking questions that don't matter any - way,

Bm   E   Am⁷   D
Just give us a kiss to celebrate here today."

Am⁷   D   D
Something changed.

```
        |  G        |  G              ‖
```

Instrumental ‖: G | G | Bm | C   :‖

Verse 3

                      C   D
When we woke up that morning
           Bm   E
We had no way of knowing,
                  C   D
That in a matter of hours
            Bm   E
We'd change the way we were going,
Bm   E
  Where would I be now?
Bm   E
  Where would I be now
        Am7 D
If we'd never met?
Bm   E
  Would I be singing this song
      Am7   D
To someone else instead?
        Am7   D   D
I don't know, but like you just said,
G
  Something changed.

Substitute

Words & Music by
Pete Townshend

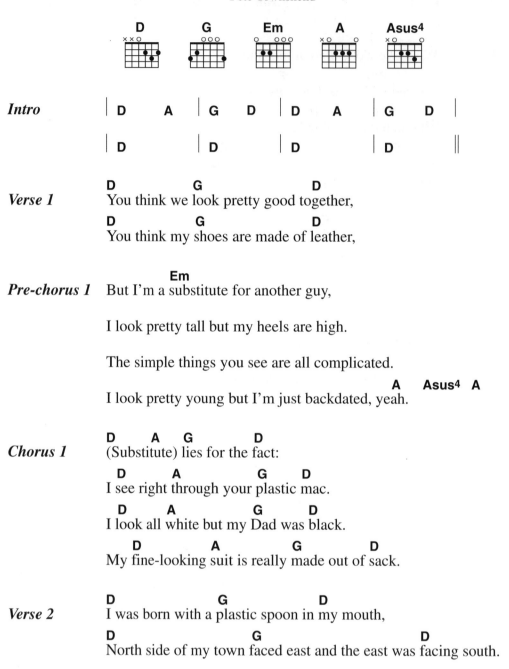

Intro
| D   A | G   D | D   A | G   D |
| D | D | D | D |

Verse 1

D   G   D
You think we look pretty good together,

D   G   D
You think my shoes are made of leather,

Pre-chorus 1

                     Em
But I'm a substitute for another guy,

I look pretty tall but my heels are high.

The simple things you see are all complicated.

                                        A   Asus4 A
I look pretty young but I'm just backdated, yeah.

Chorus 1

D   A G   D
(Substitute) lies for the fact:

    D   A   G   D
I see right through your plastic mac.

    D   A   G   D
I look all white but my Dad was black.

      D   A   G   D
My fine-looking suit is really made out of sack.

Verse 2

D   G   D
I was born with a plastic spoon in my mouth,

D   G   D
North side of my town faced east and the east was facing south.

Pre-chorus 2

                  Em
And now you dare to look me in the eye

But crocodile tears are what you cry.

If it's a genuine problem you won't try

To work it out at all, just pass it by,

      A Asus4 A
Pass it by.

Chorus 2

    D   **A** **G**   **D**
(Substitute) me for him,

    D   **A**   **G**   **D**
(Substitute) my Coke for gin.

    D   **A**   **G**   **D**
(Substitute) you fooled my Mum,

      D   **A**   **G**   **D**
At least I'll get my washing done.

Solo   ‖: **D** | **G** | **D** | **D**   :‖

Pre-chorus 3   As Pre-chorus 1

Link   ‖: **D** **A** | **G** **D** | **D** **A** | **G** **D** :‖

Verse 3   As Verse 2

Pre-chorus 4   As Pre-chorus 2

Chorus 3   As Chorus 2

Chorus 4   As Chorus 1

Take A Chance On Me

Words & Music by
Benny Andersson & Björn Ulvaeus

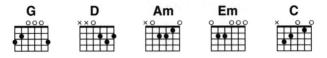

Capo fourth fret

Chorus 1

                 G
If you change your mind, I'm the first in line,

Honey, I'm still free,
          D
Take a chance on me.

If you need me, let me know, gonna be around,
                 G
If you got no place to go when you're feeling down.

If you're all alone when the pretty birds have flown,

Honey, I'm still free,
          D
Take a chance on me,

Gonna do my very best and it ain't no lie,
              G
If you put me to the test, if you let me try.
  Am   **D**
Take a chance on me,
  Am   **D**
Take a chance on me.

Verse 1

Am
We can go dancing, we can go walking,
  G
As long as we're together.
Am
Listen to some music, maybe just talking,
  G
You'd get to know me better.

cont.   'Cause you know I got

Em
  So much that I wanna do,

C
  When I dream I'm alone with you,

    Em   **C**   **D**
It's ma - gic.

Em
  You want me to leave it there,

C
  Afraid of a love affair,

    Am   **D**
But I think you know

    Am   **D**
That I can't let go.

Chorus 2   As Chorus 1

          Am
Verse 2   Oh you can take your time baby, I'm in no hurry,

  G
I know I'm gonna get you.

Am
You don't wanna hurt me, baby don't worry,

G
I ain't gonna let you.

Let me tell you now,

Em
  My love is strong enough,

C
  To last when things are rough,

    Em   **C**   **D**
It's ma - gic.

Em
  You say that I waste my time,

C
  But I can't get you off my mind,

    Am   **D**
No I can't let go,

      Am   **D**
'Cause I love you so.

Chorus 3   **G**
If you change your mind, I'm the first in line,

Honey, I'm still free,
              D
Take a chance on me.

If you need me, let me know, gonna be around,
                    G
If you got no place to go when you're feeling down.

If you're all alone when the pretty birds have flown,

Honey, I'm still free,
              D
Take a chance on me,

Gonna do my very best,

Baby can't you see?

Gotta put me to the test,
     G
Take a chance on me.

Outro   **G**
:||: Ba ba ba ba baa, ba ba ba ba baa,

Honey I'm still free,
             D
Take a chance on me.

Gonna do my very best,

Baby can't you see?

Gotta put me to the test,
     G
Take a chance on me.   :|| *Repeat to fade*

A Thousand Trees

Words by Kelly Jones
Music by Kelly Jones, Richard Jones & Stuart Cable

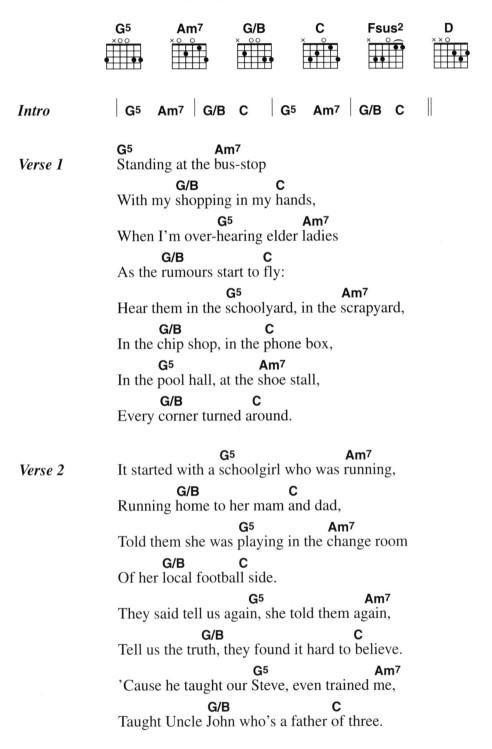

G5   Am7   G/B   C   Fsus2   D

Intro | G5   Am7 | G/B   C | G5   Am7 | G/B   C ||

Verse 1

G5   Am7
Standing at the bus-stop
          G/B   C
With my shopping in my hands,
                    G5   Am7
When I'm over-hearing elder ladies
          G/B   C
As the rumours start to fly:
                    G5   Am7
Hear them in the schoolyard, in the scrapyard,
          G/B   C
In the chip shop, in the phone box,
          G5   Am7
In the pool hall, at the shoe stall,
          G/B   C
Every corner turned around.

Verse 2

                    G5   Am7
It started with a schoolgirl who was running,
          G/B   C
Running home to her mam and dad,
                    G5   Am7
Told them she was playing in the change room
          G/B   C
Of her local football side.
                    G5   Am7
They said tell us again, she told them again,
          G/B   C
Tell us the truth, they found it hard to believe.
                    G5   Am7
'Cause he taught our Steve, even trained me,
          G/B   C
Taught Uncle John who's a father of three.

Chorus 1

        Am⁷   **Fsus²**   **C**
Only takes one tree to make a thousand matches,

        Am⁷   **Fsus² C**   **G⁵**   **Am⁷ G/B C**
Only takes one match to burn a thousand ____ trees,

   G⁵   **Am⁷ G/B C**
Thousand trees. ____

Verse 3

        G⁵   **Am⁷**
See it in the classroom or the swimming pool

     G/B   **C**
Where the matchstick men are made.

    G⁵   **Am⁷**
At the Scouts' hall, at the football,

     G/B   **C**
Where the wise we trust are paid.

       G⁵   **Am⁷**
They all honour his name, did a lot for the game,

     G/B   **C**
He had his name knocked up above the sports ground gates.

     G⁵   **Am⁷**
Now they're ripping them down, stamping the ground.

G/B   **C**
Picture gathers dust in the bar in the lounge.

Chorus 2

      Am⁷   **Fsus²**   **C**
It takes one tree to make a thousand matches,

       Am⁷   **Fsus² C**   **G⁵**   **Am⁷ G/B C**
Only takes one match to burn a thousand ____ trees,

   G⁵   **Am⁷ G/B C**
Thousand trees. ____

Bridge

D   **Fsus²**   **C**
  Wake up,   smell the rain.

D   **Fsus²** **C**
  Shake up, he's back to stay.

D   **Fsus²** **C**
  Hasn't been on a holi - day,

D   **Fsus²**   **C**
  Growing seeds don't believe why he's

G⁵   **Am⁷**   **G/B C**
Been __ a - way. ____

Link

‖: **G⁵**   **Am⁷** | **G/B** **C** :‖ *Play 3 times*

Verse 4

G5   Am7
In the schoolyard, change room,

G/B   C
Playing fields, bathroom,

G5   Am7
Phone box, office blocks,

G/B   C
Corners turned around.

                    G5   Am7
They keep doubting the flame, tossing the blame.

          G/B   C
Got his name knocked up above the sports ground gates,

             G5   Am7
Now they're ripping them down, stamping the ground,

G/B   C
Picture gathers dust in the bar in the lounge.

Chorus 3

    Am7   Fsus2   C
It takes one tree to make a thousand matches,

      Am7   Fsus2 C   G5 Am7 G/B C
Only takes one match to burn a thousand ____ trees,

    G5 Am7 G/B C
Thousand trees, ____

    G5 Am7 G/B C
Thousand trees, ____

    G5 Am7 G/B   C
Thousand ____ trees. ____

Waiting In Vain

Words & Music by
Bob Marley

Chords: A♭maj7   D♭maj7   D♭   E♭   Cm7   B♭m7

Intro

| A♭maj7 | D♭maj7 | A♭maj7 | D♭maj7 ‖

Chorus 1

A♭maj7   D♭maj7
I don't wanna wait in vain for your love;
A♭maj7   D♭maj7
I don't wanna wait in vain for your love.

Verse 1

A♭maj7   D♭maj7
From the very first time I rest my eyes on you, girl,
A♭maj7   D♭maj7
My heart says follow through.
A♭maj7   D♭maj7
But I know, now, that I'm way down on your line,
A♭maj7   D♭maj7
But the waitin' feel is fine:
A♭maj7   D♭maj7
So don't treat me like a puppet on a string,
A♭maj7   D♭maj7
'Cause I know I have to do my thing.
A♭maj7   D♭maj7
Don't talk to me as if you think I'm dumb;
A♭maj7   D♭maj7
I wanna know when you're gonna come.

Chorus 2

A♭maj7   D♭maj7
See, I don't wanna wait in vain for your love;
A♭maj7   D♭maj7
I don't wanna wait in vain for your love;
A♭maj7   D♭maj7
I don't wanna wait in vain for your love,

Bridge

          D♭   E♭
'Cause if summer is here,

Cm7   B♭m7
I'm still waiting there;

D♭   E♭
  Winter is here,

      Cm7   B♭m7
And I'm still waiting there.

Solo

| A♭maj7 | D♭maj7 | A♭maj7 | D♭maj7 |

| A♭maj7 | D♭maj7 | A♭maj7 | D♭maj7 ‖

                                Like I said:

Verse 2

A♭maj7   D♭maj7
  It's been three years since I'm knockin' on your door,

A♭maj7   D♭maj7
  And I still can knock some more:

A♭maj7   D♭maj7
Ooh girl, ooh girl, is it feasible? I wanna know now,

A♭maj7   D♭maj7
  For I to knock some more.

        A♭maj7   D♭maj7
Ya see, in life I know there's lots of grief,

A♭maj7   D♭maj7
  But your love is my relief:

A♭maj7   D♭maj7
Tears in my eyes burn, tears in my eyes burn

        A♭maj7   D♭maj7
While I'm waiting, while I'm waiting for my turn,

See!

Chorus 3

‖: A♭maj7   D♭maj7
  I don't wanna wait in vain for your love;

A♭maj7   D♭maj7
I don't wanna wait in vain for your love, oh! :‖ *Play 4 times*

Coda

‖: A♭maj7
  I don't wanna, I don't wanna, I don't wanna, I don't wanna,

D♭maj7
I don't wanna wait in vain. :‖ *Play 4 times*

‖:   A♭maj7
  It's your love that I'm waiting on,

        D♭maj7
It's my love that you're running from. :‖ *Repeat to fade*

What Can I Do

Words & Music by
Andrea Corr, Caroline Corr, Sharon Corr & Jim Corr

A   E   D   Bm7   F#m   Dmaj7

Intro

A
Do do do do

E
do do do do

D
Do do do   do do do,

A
Do do do do

E
do do do do

Bm7
Do do do   do do do.

Verse 1

A   E   D
I haven't slept at all in days

A   E   Bm7
It's been so long since we've talked

A   E   D
And I have been here many ti____ mes

A   E   Bm7
I just don't know what I'm doing wrong.

Chorus 1

A   E   D
What can I do to make you love me?

A   E   Bm7
What can I do to make you care?

A   E   D
What can I say to make you feel this?

A   E   Bm7
What can I do to get you there?

Verse 2

A   E   D
There's only so much I can take

A   E   Bm7
And I just got to let it go,

A   E   D
And who knows I might feel better, yea - - eah

A   E   Bm7
If I don't try and I don't hope.

Chorus 2   As Chorus 1

Bridge

F♯m   Dmaj⁷ E Dmaj⁷ E
No more waiting, no more aching _____

F♯m   Dmaj⁷ E Dmaj⁷ E
No more fighting, no more trying _____

Verse 3

A   D
Maybe there's nothing more to say

A   E   Bm⁷
And in a funny way I'm caught

A   E   D
Because the power is not mine

A   E   Bm⁷
I'm just gonna let it fly.

Chorus 3

A   E   D
What can I do to make you love me?

A   E   Bm⁷
What can I do to make you care?

A   E   D
What can I say to make you feel this?

A   E   Bm⁷
What can I do to get you there?

Chorus 4

A   E   D
What can I do to make you love me?

A   E   Bm⁷
What can I do to make you care?

A   E   D
What can I change to make you feel this?

A   E   Bm⁷   Dmaj⁷ E F♯m E
What can I do to get you there and lo - ove me? _____ (love me).

Coda

                Dmaj⁷ E   F♯m E
Lo - o - o - ve me,   love me. *Repeat to fade*

You Really Got Me

Words & Music by
Ray Davies

F5   G5   A   G   C   D

Intro   F5 ‖: G5 F5 G5 F5 | G5 F5 G5 F5 :‖

Verse 1

G5 F5 G5   F5 G5   F5   G5 F5 G5
Girl, ___ you really got me goin',

     F5 G5 F5 G5   F5 G5 F5 G5
You got me so I don't know what I'm doin'.

F5 G5 F5 G5   F5 G5   F5   G5
  Yeah,___ you really got me now,

     F5 G5 F5 G5   F5 G5 F5 G5
You got me so I can't sleep at night.

A G A   G A   G   A
Yeah, ___ you really got me now,

    G A G   A   G A   G A
You got me so I don't know what I'm doin', now.

  C D C D   C D   C   D
Oh yeah, ___ you really got me now,

    C D C   D
You got me so I can't sleep at night.

Chorus 1

C   D   C D
You really got me,

C   D   C D
You really got me,

C   D   C D   C
You really got me.

Verse 2

G5 F5 G5   F5 G5   F5   G5 F5 G5
See, ___ don't ever set me free,

   F5   G5   F5 G5   F5 G5 F5 G5
I always wanna be by your side.

F5 G5 F5 G5   F5 G5   F5   G5
 Girl, ___ you really got me now,

       F5 G5 F5   G5   F5 G5 F5 G5
You got me so I can't sleep at night.

A G A   G A   G   A
Yeah, ___ you really got me now,

      G A G   A   G A   G A
You got me so I don't know what I'm doin',   now.

  C D C D   C D   C   D
Oh yeah, ___ you really got me now,

      C   D C   D
You got me so I can't sleep at night.

Chorus 2   *As Chorus 1*

Oh no…

Solo   ‖: G5 F5 G5 F5 | G5 F5 G5 F5 :‖ *Play 5 times*

Verse 3   *As Verse 2*

             C   D   C D
Chorus 3   You really got me,

             C   D   C D
             You really got me,

             C   D   C D
             You really got me.

43

You're Still The One

Words & Music by
Shania Twain & R.J. Lange

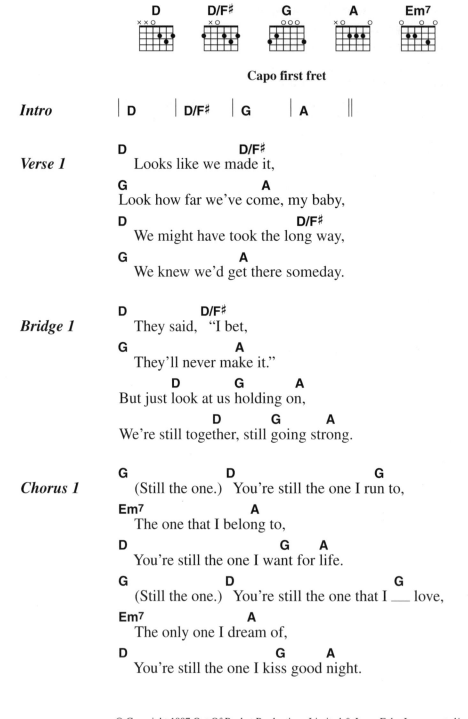

Capo first fret

Intro | D | D/F♯ | G | A ‖

Verse 1

D   D/F♯
Looks like we made it,

G   A
Look how far we've come, my baby,

D   D/F♯
We might have took the long way,

G   A
We knew we'd get there someday.

Bridge 1

D   D/F♯
They said, "I bet,

G   A
They'll never make it."

          D   G   A
But just look at us holding on,

               D   G   A
We're still together, still going strong.

Chorus 1

G   D   G
(Still the one.) You're still the one I run to,

Em⁷   A
The one that I belong to,

D   G   A
You're still the one I want for life.

G   D   G
(Still the one.) You're still the one that I ＿ love,

Em⁷   A
The only one I dream of,

D   G   A
You're still the one I kiss good night.

Verse 2

```
D                       D/F♯
  Ain't nothing better,
G             A
  We beat the odds together,
D                       D/F♯
  I'm glad we didn't listen,
G                 A
  Look at what we would be missing.
```

Bridge 2   As Bridge 1

Chorus 2

```
G                   D                     G
  (Still the one.)  You're still the one I run to,
Em⁷                 A
  The one that I belong to,
D                       G     A
  You're still the one I want for life.
G                   D                     G
  (Still the one.)  You're still the one that I __ love,
Em⁷                 A
  The only one I dream of,
D                       G      A
  You're still the one I kiss good night,

  You're still the one.
```

Solo   ‖: D | G | A | A   :‖

Chorus 3

```
G                   D                     G
  (Still the one.)  You're still the one I run to,
Em⁷                 A
  The one that I belong to,
D                       G     A
  You're still the one I want for life.
G                   D                     G
  (Still the one.)  You're still the one that I __ love,
Em⁷                 A
  The only one I dream of,
D                       G      A
  You're still the one I kiss good night,
D                   D/F♯
  I'm so glad we made it,
G                 A
Look how far we've come, my baby.
```

Torn

Words & Music by
Anne Preven, Scott Cutler & Phil Thornalley

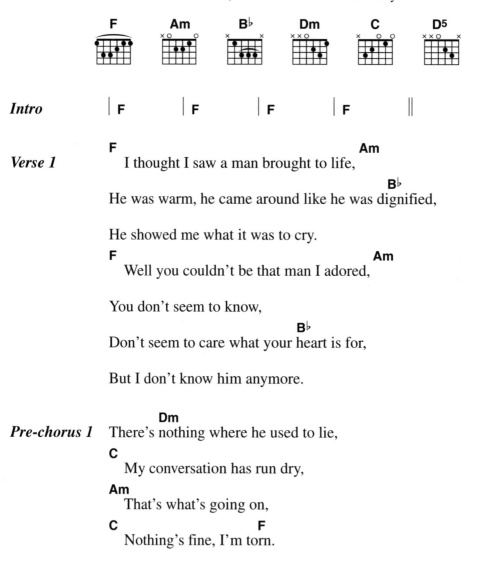

Intro　　　| F　　　| F　　　| F　　　| F　　　||

Verse 1

F　　　　　　　　　　　　　　　　　　　　Am
　　I thought I saw a man brought to life,

　　　　　　　　　　　　　　　　　　　　　　　　　　B♭
　He was warm, he came around like he was dignified,

　He showed me what it was to cry.

F　　　　　　　　　　　　　　　　　　Am
　　Well you couldn't be that man I adored,

　You don't seem to know,

　　　　　　　　　　　　　　　　B♭
　Don't seem to care what your heart is for,

　But I don't know him anymore.

Pre-chorus 1

　　　　　　　　　Dm
There's nothing where he used to lie,

　C
　　My conversation has run dry,

　Am
　　That's what's going on,

　C　　　　　　　　　　　　F
　　Nothing's fine, I'm torn.

Chorus 1

                                  C
I'm all out of faith,

                  Dm
This is how I feel,

                        B♭
I'm cold and I am shamed

                        F
Lying naked on the floor.

                      C   **Dm**
Illusion never changed into something real,

          B♭   **F**
Wide awake and I _ can see the perfect sky is torn,

                C
You're a little late,

                Dm
I'm already torn.

Verse 2

    F   **Am**
    So I guess the fortune teller's right.

I should have seen just what was there

                  B♭
And not some holy light,

But you crawled beneath my veins.

Pre-chorus 2

                  Dm
And now I don't care, I had no luck,

C
   I don't miss it all that much,

Am
   There's just so many things

C   **F**
   That I can search, I'm torn.

Chorus 2   As Chorus 1

Dm   **B♭**
Torn

D5   **F**   **C**
Oo, oo, oo. _____

                    Dm
Pre-chorus 3   There's nothing where he used to lie,

                 C
                    My inspiration has run dry,

                 Am
                   That's what's going on,

                 C   **F**
                   Nothing's right, I'm torn.

                             C
Chorus 3   I'm all out of faith,

                             Dm
                 This is how I feel,

                                   B♭
                 I'm cold and I am shamed,

                                 F
                 Lying naked on the floor.

                             C   **Dm**
                 Illusion never changed into something real,

                             B♭   **F**
                 Wide awake and I _ can see the perfect sky is torn.

                             C
Chorus 4   I'm all out of faith,

                             Dm
                 This is how I feel,

                                   B♭
                 I'm cold and I'm ashamed,

                                     F
                 Bound and broken on the floor.

                             C
                 You're a little late,

                             Dm   **B**♭
                 I'm already torn…

                 Dm   **C**
                 Torn…

                 Repeat Chorus ad lib. to fade